Piano Star 3

24 pieces for young pianists
Prep Test level to Grade 1

Compiled and edited by
David Blackwell and Aisling Greally

Illustrations by Tim Budgen

Welcome to Piano Star

To the teacher: Our aim in this series is to present an exciting range of appealing and accessible new pieces which will inspire young pianists and help them to develop their musical skills. The first book is suitable for learners who have completed, or nearly completed, their first tutor book; the second is at ABRSM Prep Test level and provides alternative repertoire for that assessment; the third book moves players towards Grade 1.

Each book presents original compositions and newly arranged pieces by a host of leading composers, all designed to capture the young imagination. There is also a sprinkling of duets for pupil and teacher to play together, many of which can also be played as solos. Activities dotted throughout the books provide extension ideas to enhance children's creative response to and engagement with the pieces.

The variety of repertoire provides a rich mix of musical styles, and within this we have sought to offer practical pieces that support the technical level of pupils at different stages. Each book progressively introduces a range of suitable techniques, such as different hand positions and shifts, varied articulations, simple chords and part-writing. The result is a wealth of useful teaching material which children will love to play.

We should like to thank all our highly creative composers, Claire Webb at ABRSM for steering this project so deftly, Ruth Gerald and the numerous other reviewers who commented on early drafts, and Karen Marshall, who so generously shared her time and expertise. We hope that you and your pupils enjoy *Piano Star*!

David Blackwell and Aisling Greally

Book and cover design by Kate Benjamin
Music origination by Moira Roach
Illustrations by Tim Budgen, represented by Good Illustration Ltd
Copyright © Tim Budgen

First published in 2016 by ABRSM (Publishing) Ltd, a wholly owned subsidiary of ABRSM
© 2016 by The Associated Board of the Royal Schools of Music

Reprinted in 2017

ISBN 978 1 84849 942 3
AB 3878

Printed in England by Page Bros (Norwich) Ltd, on materials from sustainable sources

Contents

Dance of the Pianists (duet)	Alan Bullard	4
Cherry Blossom	David Blackwell	6
Squirmy Worms	Peter Gritton	7
Rigadoon	Henry Purcell, arr. David Blackwell	8
Haunted House	Peter Gritton	9
Echo Blues (duet)	Mike Cornick	10
The Fridge Monster	Mark Tanner	12
Morning Has Broken (duet)	Trad. Scottish, arr. David Blackwell	13
The Lonely Bear	John Madden	14
Halloween Dance	Mike Cornick	15
Lost in the Maze (duet)	Mark Tanner	16
Kangaroo Barbecue	David Blackwell	18
Wonderful World!	David Blackwell	19
You'll Never Get to Heaven...	Trad., arr. Karen Marshall	20
Special Place	Edmund Jolliffe	21
Head in the Clouds	Andrew Eales	22
Carnival Time	Nikki Iles	23
Strange Creatures (duet)	Edmund Jolliffe	24
The Old Typewriter	Peter Gritton	26
Cat Burglar	Edmund Jolliffe	27
Little Hummingbird (duet)	Nikki Iles	28
May Song	Trad., arr. Nancy Litten	30
Pirates Coming!	Edmund Jolliffe	31
Panda Percussion	Nancy Litten	32

Dance of the Pianists

Alan Bullard

Pupil part

ACTIVITY

Listen to how the quavers dance from one player to the other.
Mark on the music where the duet part has quavers while you play longer notes.

Duet part

Happily

Cherry Blossom

David Blackwell

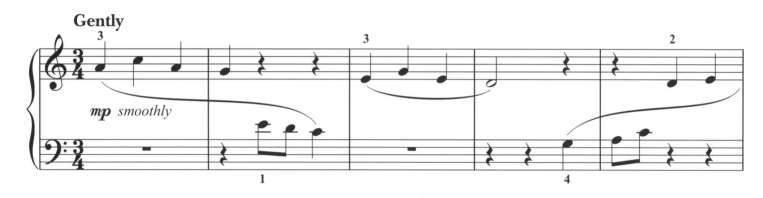

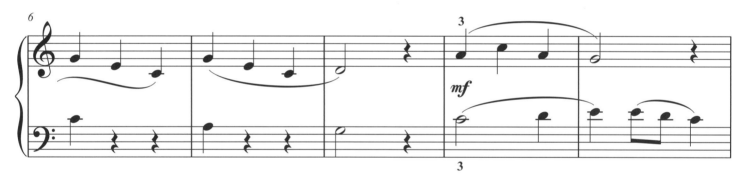

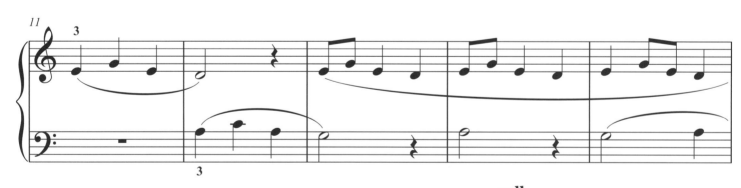

Squirmy Worms

Music and words by
Peter Gritton

Smooth and slithering

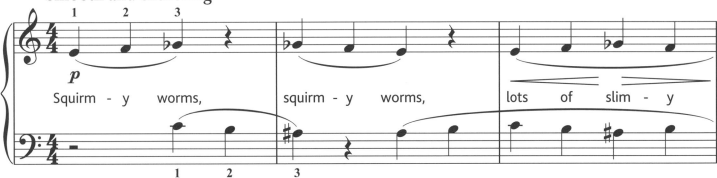

Squirm - y worms, squirm - y worms, lots of slim - y

squirm - y worms! Wrig-gl-ing a - long, wrig-gl-ing a - long,

Worms that wrig - gle - squig - gle through my song!

ACTIVITY

Did you know that notes on the piano can have more than one name?
For example, F sharp can also be called G flat. Write down two different names for each of the five black keys.

....

Rigadoon

Henry Purcell (1659–95)
arr. David Blackwell

Haunted House

Peter Gritton

* Slowly play the notes of the chord from bottom to top, as quietly as possible, to make a ghostly sound.

Echo Blues

Duet part

Echo Blues

Mike Cornick

Pupil part

* See inside back cover.

The Fridge Monster

Mark Tanner

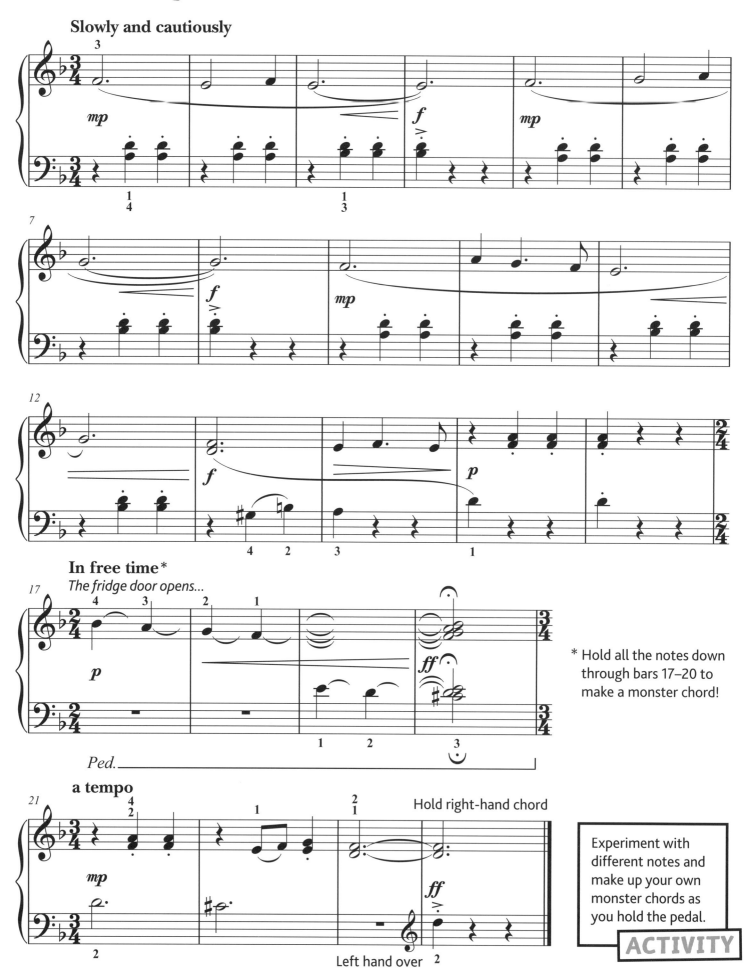

* Hold all the notes down through bars 17–20 to make a monster chord!

Experiment with different notes and make up your own monster chords as you hold the pedal.

ACTIVITY

Morning Has Broken

Traditional Scottish
arr. David Blackwell

Pupil part

Duet part

The Lonely Bear

John Madden

Quite slowly

Halloween Dance

Mike Cornick

Lost in the Maze

Duet part

Lost in the Maze

Mark Tanner

Pupil part

Kangaroo Barbecue

David Blackwell

To help with the rhythm of the opening, say the words 'Kangaroos having a barbecue, barbecue, barbecue'. Can you make up some words for the rest of the piece?

ACTIVITY

Wonderful World!

Music and words by
David Blackwell

You'll Never Get to Heaven...

Traditional
arr. Karen Marshall

* See inside back cover.

** Alternatively, omit tremolo and play a single E flat semibreve in this bar, with finger 2.

Special Place

Music and words by
Edmund Jolliffe

Gently ♩ = 90

Do you have a spe - cial place, se - cret from the out - side world?

Some-where on - ly you can go, some-where on - ly you will know.

There's a place I like to be, when I want to be a - lone.

Warm and hid - den, safe and calm. That is my spe - cial place.

Head in the Clouds

Andrew Eales

Walking along, deep in thought ♩ = 120

Carnival Time

Nikki Iles

Strange Creatures

Edmund Jolliffe

Pupil part

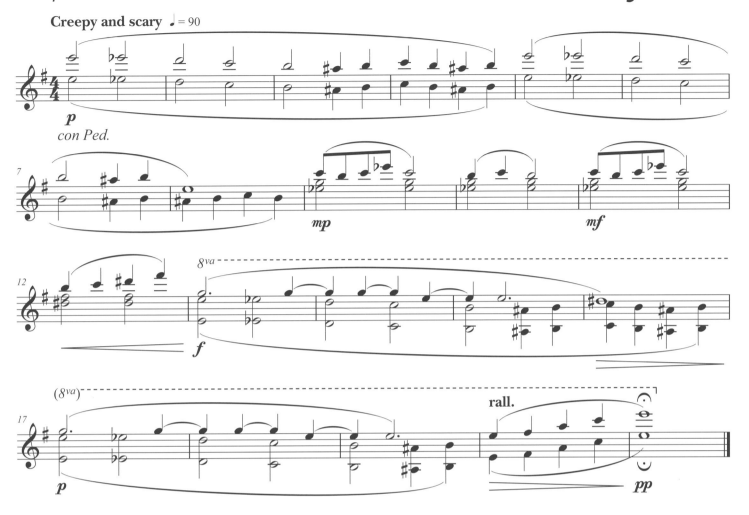

The Old Typewriter

Peter Gritton

- Old typewriters used to 'ping' when you reached the end of the line.
- At the end of the piece, pretend that the typewriter has fallen off the table!

Con moto ♩ = 100

Listen to and watch a YouTube video of *The Typewriter* by Leroy Anderson, and see a typewriter played as a percussion instrument!

ACTIVITY

* Aim for a high D, but if you miss, it doesn't matter! Just keep in time. ** Aim for a low G!

Cat Burglar

Also try this piece using swing quavers (see inside back cover). **ACTIVITY**

Edmund Jolliffe

Steady and cool ♩ = 100

p

Left hand like a plucked double bass

mf

f

mf

p

* Play the notes of the chord from bottom to top.

Little Hummingbird

Duet part

With quiet joy (gentle Township)

Little Hummingbird

Nikki Iles

Pupil part

- Play an octave higher than written when playing with the duet part.

With quiet joy (gentle Township)

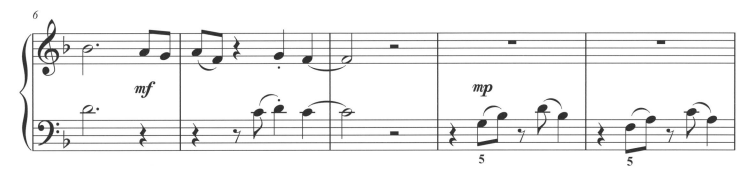

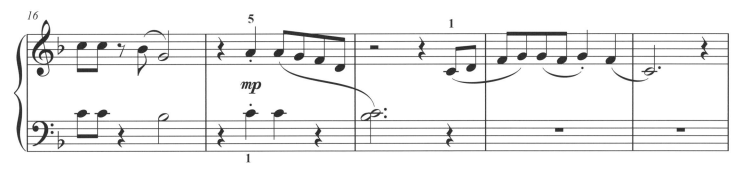

May Song

Traditional
arr. Nancy Litten

Happily

Pirates Coming!

Edmund Jolliffe

Fast and exciting ♩ = 144

Panda Percussion

Nancy Litten

Hold the pedal at the end to let the sound ring on